Georgia

This book belongs to ....

3

OXFORD
UNIVERSITY PRESS

Great Clarendon Street, Oxford, OX2 6DP, United Kingdom

Oxford University Press is a department of the University of Oxford.
It furthers the University's objective of excellence in research, scholarship and
education by publishing worldwide. Oxford is a registered trade mark of Oxford
University Press in the UK and in certain other countries

British Library Cataloguing in Publication Data
Data available

ISBN: 978-0-19-273605-5

10 9 8 7 6 5 4 3 2 1

Typeset in OUP Earlybird

Printed in China

Paper used in the production of this book is a natural, recyclable product
made from wood grown in sustainable forests. The manufacturing process
conforms to the environmental regulations of the country of origin.

Acknowledgements

Series Advisor: Nikki Gamble

Help your child's learning
with essential tips, phonics
support and free eBooks
www.oxfordowl.co.uk

Traditional Tales

Chicken Licken

and Other Stories

OXFORD
UNIVERSITY PRESS

Tips for reading Chicken Licken together

This story is a simple retelling of 'Chicken Licken', which is a story that has several versions and is known in the USA as 'Chicken Little'.

This book practises these sounds:

ar (as in 'barn')   **ee** (as in 'see')   **ow** (as in 'ow!')

Ask your child to point to these letter pairs and say the sounds.

Your child might find these words tricky:

we me they all you   Say these words for your child if they do not know them.

- Before you begin, ask your child to read the title to you by sounding out and blending. Talk about what the story might be about. What kind of animal is Chicken Licken?

- Encourage your child to read the story to you. Talk about the pictures as you read.

- Your child will be able to read most of the words in the story, but if they struggle with a word, remind them to say the sounds in the word from left to right. Ask them to point to the sounds as they say them, and then blend the sounds into a whole word, e.g. ch-i-ck-en.

- After you have read the story look through it again and ask your child 'Which animal is the most sensible in the story?' Talk about how Chicken Licken can see that he has made a mistake.

- Do the 'Retell the story' activity together!

Chicken Licken

Written by Gill Munton

Illustrated by Christine Pym

OXFORD
UNIVERSITY PRESS

Tock!

8

9

Chicken Licken ran to the barn.

Chicken Licken and Hen Len
ran to the farmyard.

Cock Lock!
The sun fell on me!
Shall we go and
tell Duck Luck?

13

They all ran back to the garden.

17

19

A nut,
Chicken Licken!

Encourage your child to retell the story in their own words using the pictures as prompts. You could do this together, or take it in turns. Have fun!

Once upon a time...

The end.

Tips for reading Right for Me together

This story is a simple retelling of 'Goldilocks and the Three Bears', an English folktale written down almost 200 years ago.

This book practises these sounds:

igh (as in 'right')   **or** (as in 'for')   **oo** (as in 'room')

ee (as in 'see')   **air** (as in 'chair')

Ask your child to point to these letter groups and say the sounds.

Your child might find these words tricky:

they   me   my   Say these words for your child if they do not know them.

- Before you begin, ask your child to read the title to you by sounding out and blending. Talk about what the story might be about. What do you think the girl is doing? What might be right for her?

- Encourage your child to read the story to you. Talk about the pictures as you read.

- Your child will be able to read most of the words in the story, but if they struggle with a word, remind them to say the sounds in the word from left to right. Ask them to point to the sounds as they say them, and then blend the sounds into a whole word, e.g. b-e-d-r-oo-m.

- After you have read the story look through it again and ask your child 'Which three things were right for the little girl?' Can they find the pages that tell us?

- Do the 'Retell the story' activity together!

Right for Me

Written by Gill Munton

Illustrated by Ilaria Falorsi

OXFORD
UNIVERSITY PRESS

I am in the wood!
La la la ...

I can see a log cabin!
I will go in.

28

This dish is
no good!

This dish is
no good!

This is the right
dish for me!

Ted

Mum

Dad

This chair is
no good!

This chair is
no good!

This is the right chair for me!

I will go into the bedroom.

This bed is
no good!

This bed is
no good!

This is the right bed for me!

Zzzzz

Tum tee tum …

37

39

Retell the story

Encourage your child to retell the story in their own words using the pictures as prompts. You could do this together, or take it in turns. Have fun!

Once upon a time...

The end.

41

Tips for reading Boxer and the Fish together

About the story

This story is a simple retelling of Aesop's fable 'The Greedy Dog'.

This book practises these sounds:

er (as in 'bigger') **oo** (as in 'look') **or** (as in 'for')

ar (as in 'park') **ow** (as in 'town') **oo** (as in 'food')

oa (as in 'road') **ee** (as in 'deep')

Ask your child to point to these letter groups and say the sounds.

- Before you begin, ask your child to read the title to you by sounding out and blending. Talk about what the story might be about. Who is the dog? Where might he have got the fish from?

- Encourage your child to read the story to you. Talk about the pictures as you read.

- Your child will be able to read most of the words in the story, but if they struggle with a word, remind them to say the sounds in the word from left to right. Ask them to point to the sounds as they say them, and then blend the sounds into a whole word, e.g. d-ow-n.

- After you have read the story look through it again and talk about what happened. Talk about who you feel sorry for in the story, Boxer or the fishmonger? How do we know that Boxer was a greedy dog?

- Do the 'Retell the story' activity together!

Boxer and the Fish

Written by Monica Hughes

Illustrated by Ann Ruozhu Sun

Boxer was a big dog.

Boxer ran into town to look for food.

In a shop was ...

Boxer took the fish
and ran off.

He ran down the road.

Boxer ran into the park.

In the park was a deep pool.

Boxer took a good look. In the deep pool was ...

... a dog!

The fish fell in the pool.

No! My fish!

Boxer was sad.

No dinner
for me!

Encourage your child to retell the story in their own words using the pictures as prompts. You could do this together, or take it in turns. Have fun!

Once upon a time...

58

The end.

Tips for reading Cook, Pot, Cook! together

About the story

This story is a simple retelling of 'The Magic Porridge Pot' by the Brothers Grimm.

This book practises these sounds:

oo (as in 'cook')   **oi** (as in 'boil')   **oo** (as in 'food')

igh (as in 'night')   **oa** (as in 'road')   **er** (as in 'supper')

ear (as in 'dear')   **air** (as in 'chair')   **ow** (as in 'down')

Ask your child to point to these letter groups and say the sounds.

- Before you begin, ask your child to read the title to you by sounding out and blending. Talk about what the story might be about. What do you think the pot might do?

- Encourage your child to read the story to you. Talk about the pictures as you read.

- Your child will be able to read most of the words in the story, but if they struggle with a word, remind them to say the sounds in the word from left to right. Ask them to point to the sounds as they say them, and then blend the sounds into a whole word, e.g. b-oi-l-i-ng.

- After you have read the story look through it again and talk about what happened. Do you think Nan seemed upset about what she had done? Will they use the pot again?

- Do the 'Retell the story' activity together!

Cook, Pot, Cook!

Written by David Bedford

Illustrated by Jimothy Rolovio

OXFORD
UNIVERSITY PRESS

Tess got a pot.

The pot was boiling.

Look at all the food, Mum!

67

That night ...

The pot was full!
It did not stop!

Look at all the
food, Mum!

71

The food got to Nan in her chair.

Look at all the food, Nan!

The food took Nan
down the road.

73

Retell the story

Encourage your child to retell the story in their own words using the pictures as prompts. You could do this together, or take it in turns. Have fun!

Once upon a time...

The end.

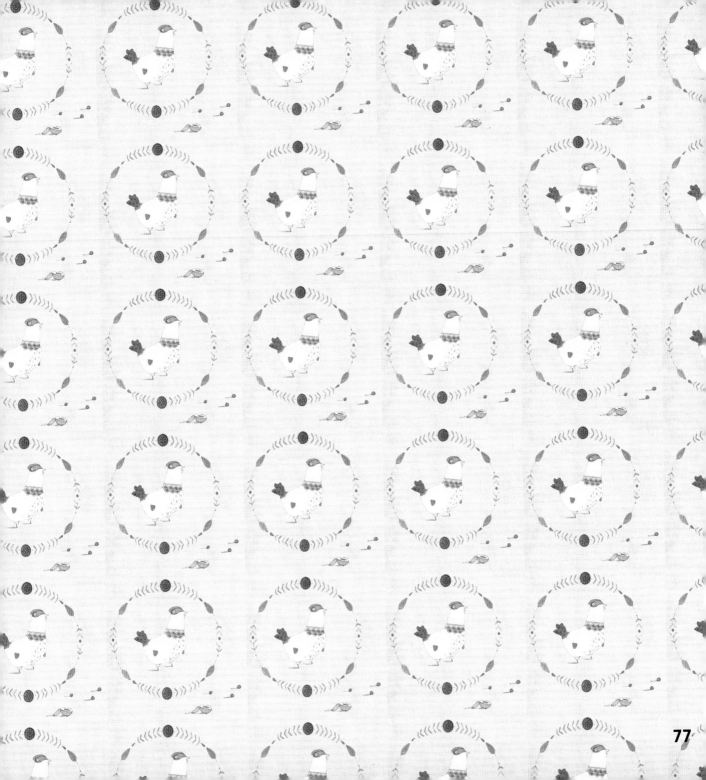

Practise Your Phonics With
Traditional Tales

More stories for you to enjoy...

Practise Your Phonics With
Traditional Tales
Stage 1+

The Gingerbread Man
and Other Stories

4 stories you can read by yourself!
OXFORD

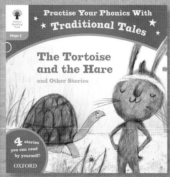

Practise Your Phonics With
Traditional Tales
Stage 2

The Tortoise and the Hare
and Other Stories

4 stories you can read by yourself!
OXFORD

Practise Your Phonics With
Traditional Tales
Stage 3

Chicken Licken
and Other Stories

4 stories you can read by yourself!
OXFORD

Practise Your Phonics With
Traditional Tales
Stage 4

The Man, the Boy and the Donkey
and Other Stories

4 stories you can read by yourself!
OXFORD

Coming soon...

Practise Your Phonics With
Traditional Tales

Jack and the Beanstalk
and Other Stories

4 stories you can read by yourself!
OXFORD

Practise Your Phonics With
Traditional Tales

How the Bear Lost His Tail
and Other Stories

4 stories you can read by yourself!
OXFORD

Help your child's learning with essential tips, phonics support and free eBooks

www.oxfordowl.co.uk

78